POWER RANGERS
SUPER LEGENDS
SUMMER ANNUAL

JETIX™

www.jetix.co.uk

EGMONT
We bring stories to life

First published in Great Britain 2009 by Egmont UK Limited,
239 Kensington High Street, London W8 6SA
ISBN 978 1 4052 4518 0
10 9 8 7 6 5 4 3 2 1
Printed in Italy

CONTENTS

Artwork – concept and pencil: Lucio Leoni; ink: Michela Frare; colour: Dario Calabria.

TOP OF THE WORLD

When strange events were reported at the summit of Mount Everest, Andrew Hartford sent the **Power Rangers Operation Overdrive** team in the **S.H.A.R.C.** to investigate ...

We're over the Himalayas – and there's Everest!

SHWOOOOOMMM!

Inside the S.H.A.R.C. cockpit ...

There is no sign of that **weird lightning** up here. Shall we turn back?

No, we still need to check it out. Lightning has never been seen at the summit before.

The Rangers morphed and dropped from their craft ...

Going down!

Moments later ...

Woah! It's hard to stay upright on this ice!

And it's freezing cold, too!

The Rangers struggled to defend themselves in the icy conditions ...

This wasn't a wasted trip after all!

I had hoped to find one of the hidden **crown jewels** here at the top of the world. No such luck ...

... but then I saw the Rangers! Now ... **Ice Block!**

TZACHAMMFF!

The flashes of energy from Flurious's staff struck the Black Ranger ...

No! He's trapped in solid ice!

I'm weakened by that freak hit! We're leaving, Chillers!

Flurious and his army teleported away ...

My Drive Geyser is strong enough to crack the ice blocks!

With both Rangers free, the team left the bitter cold and returned to Base ...

Well done, everyone. Let's toast Dax for his smart work ...

I have just the thing, Sir ... **iced tea!** What's wrong? Why does no one want any?

The End

13

TRACKER POWER

Mack, the Red Ranger, needs his Overdrive Tracker. Can you lead him to it by drawing a line through the maze?

FINISH

START

MACK

Now shout the morphing call – Overdrive Accelerate!

14

Answers on page 44.

EVIL NINJA

Kamdor is a trained ninja. Add some bold colours to complete the picture. You can add some stickers, too!

Can you pretend to be a ninja like Kamdor?

POWER PAIRS

Who will find the most power pairs? Play this game with a friend to find out!

16

HOW TO PLAY

Cover each picture with a small square of card. Take turns to remove two pieces of card. If the pictures match, you keep the cards. If they don't match, replace the cards. Once all the power pairs have been found, the player with the most card pieces wins the game!

ODD ONE OUT

The Yellow Ranger has a challenge for you! Can you circle the odd one out in each row?

1
a　　b　　c　　d

2
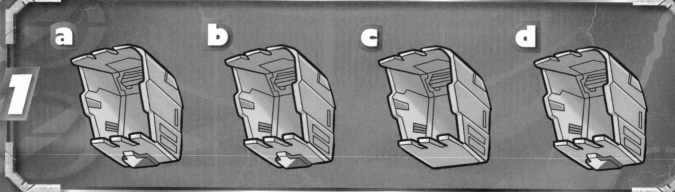

a　　b　　c　　d

3
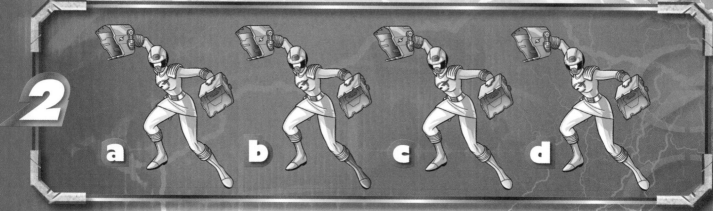

a　　b　　c　　d

Answers on page 44.

FIGHT EVIL

Look carefully at the two battle scenes. Can you find all six differences in the bottom picture? Add a blast sticker every time you spot one!

MANTICORE

Test your Ranger skills with these two
Manticore Megazord tasks!

1 How many Manticore Megazord
Flame Staffs can you count below?
Write your answer in the blast!

Which
Flame Staff
is the odd
one out?

CHALLENGE

2 Now give the Manticore some bold colours, using the coloured dots to help you.

HIT THE TARGET

Can you defeat Sculpin, one of the Ten Terrors? Shut your eyes and then, with a pen, try to land a dot on each of the targets. You have six attempts!

Award yourself one point for every target you hit, then add up your power score. Write the number in the blast!

ENERGY FIELD

Help the Blue Mystic Ranger cross the energy field to reach her Magi Staff, jumping on the blue blasts only! She can move up, down, side to side and diagonally.

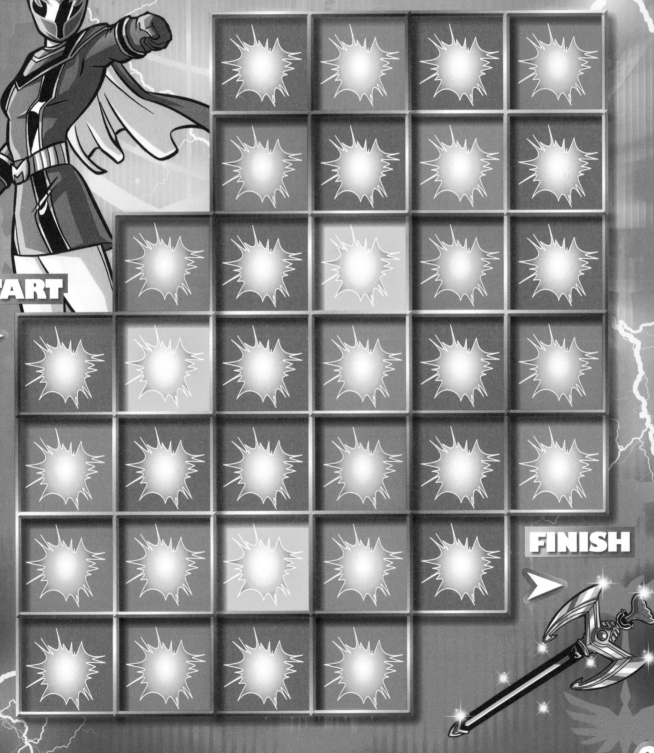

START

FINISH

Answers on page 44.

23

TYRANNO RAGE

A huge T-Rex is stomping over Reefside! Can you follow the footprint sequence and then colour in the white footprints to complete the chain?

START

FINISH

Answers on page 44.

ROCKY ROUTE

Can you help the Red Ranger safely through the rock quarry from start to finish?

START

FINISH

RAPTOR SPEED

Quick, the Red Ranger needs some powerful colours to help him race off on his Raptor Cycle! Use the picture below as a guide. You can add some stickers, too!

RANGER FINDER

How many times can you find Kira's name in the grid? Write your answer in the blast!

K	I	R	A	K
K	S	D	K	I
I	V	W	I	A
R	K	I	R	A
A	T	L	A	E

Cross off my name each time!

The Rangers were in the Megazord cockpit ...

Test successfully completed!

Have you logged the data, Kat?

Boom's on it now, Commander.

Kat's assistant, Boom, set to work as the Megazord reverted to Crawler mode ...

VRRRRRSHH!

Lurking in a nearby cave, evil weapons dealer, Broodwing, had seen everything ...

Gruumm would pay millions for that Megazord!

The Rangers set off in their Delta Runners ...

Let's step on it, guys!

Seconds later, a strange, swirling image appeared on Boom's computer ...

... sending Boom into a trance! Broodwing's voice hissed through the earpiece ...

Go to the Delta Command Megazord cockpit ...

... and lock yourself inside!

31

At the gold bank, the Rangers had combined Delta Runners.

Surrender to the Delta Squad Megazord **now!**

Meanwhile, with a brainwashed Boom at its controls, Delta Base became the Delta Command Megazord ...

VRRRRSHH!

... and charged across the city to join forces with Broodwing's robot!

ZZAWOOSHSH!

Hey! The Delta Command Megazord's supposed to be on **our** side!

Maybe Boom's computer's been rigged?

Hack into it, Kat!

Kat needed Boom's password and asked Syd for ideas ...

Try 'Orange'. Boom wants to be the Orange Ranger!

It worked!

Suddenly, a new voice rang out in Boom's ear ...

Orange Ranger, this is Commander Cruger. Destroy that raiding robot!

Broodwing tried to reverse the order ...

No! Don't listen!

But ...

ZZAVVOOSHSH!

Target destroyed!

Days later, Boom retrieved his old computer from Piggy ...

The Orange Ranger won't let this fall into enemy hands again!

Boom, I need the Megazord test data.

Yes, Sir!

I just need to press ... **uh-oh!** I hit 'delete' by mistake!

What!? Be glad you're not a Ranger. You'd be dismissed!

The End

SHADOW POWER UP

Finish colouring the Shadow Ranger to bring his powers to life. You can add stickers, too.

You never know when your Rangers skills will be needed. Stay alert at all times!

RANGER POLICE

Can you circle the S.P.D. police badges that are exactly the same?

a

b

c

d

e

f

g

PERSONAL DATA

CODE NAME
SHADOW RANGER

D-ARMS
SHADOW SABER

Answers on page 45.

S.P.D. GAME

BAT

Uh-oh! Evil Alien Battue is on the loose in Delta Base! See who will contain him first in this action-packed game.

You find your Delta Enforcer weapon. Go forwards 2 spaces.

START

You pass Battue without seeing him. Go back 1 space.

You drop your Containment Cards. Go back 2 spaces.

HOW TO PLAY

Make your own counter for each player using the helmet stickers and place them on START. You will also need a dice. The first person to roll a 6 starts. Take turns to roll the dice and move along the trail. The first player to reach the FINISH has safely contained Battue and wins the game!

You stop to load a Containment Card. Miss a turn!

Battue catches you off guard. Go back 3 spaces.

You locate Battue's position on a monitoring screen. Go forwards 1 space.

FINISH

RANGER WARRIOR

Red Ranger is in Battlizer mode! Circle the detail which doesn't appear in the big picture.

a

b

c

d

e

f

Answers on page 45.

SAMURAI CHALLENGE

The Green Samurai Ranger has two Ranger challenges for you!

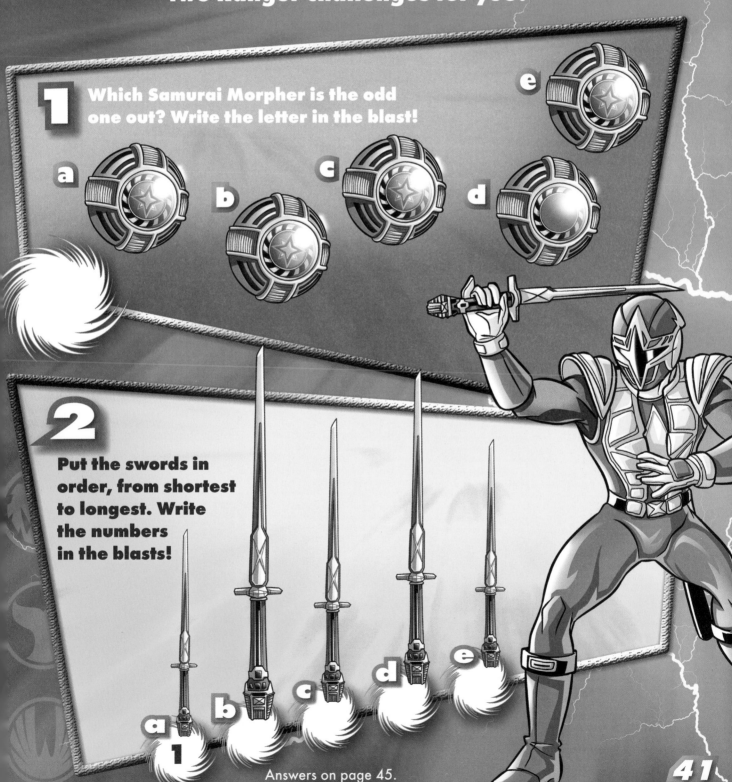

1 Which Samurai Morpher is the odd one out? Write the letter in the blast!

a b c d e

2 Put the swords in order, from shortest to longest. Write the numbers in the blasts!

a 1 b c d e

Answers on page 45.

CAMOUFLAGE CAM

Can you colour the Green Ranger so he blends into the background? How many times can you count him on this page? Write your answer in the blast!

Answers on page 45.

TALL ORDER

Can you put your stickers in the boxes
in the correct order to power up
the Storm Megazord?

© BVS Entertainment, Inc.

a

b

c

d

Answers on page 45.

ANSWERS

Page 14
TRACKER POWER

FINISH

START

Page 18
ODD ONE OUT

1 c **2** b **3** d

Page 19
FIGHT EVIL

Page 20
MANTICORE CHALLENGE
8

Page 23
ENERGY FIELD

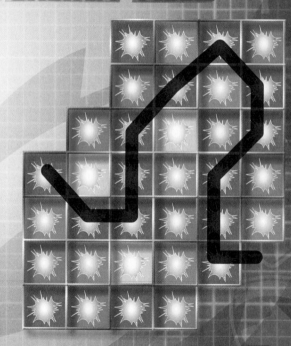

Page 24
TYRANNO RAGE

The missing colours are:

Page 25
ROCKY ROUTE

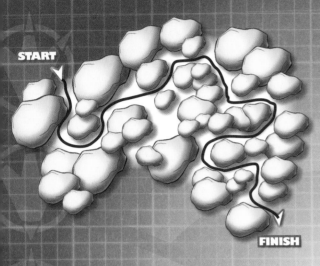

START

FINISH

Page 27
RANGER FINDER
4

Page 37
RANGER POLICE

b   d   g

Page 40
RANGER WARRIOR

e

Page 41
SAMURAI CHALLENGE

1 d

2 a e c d b

Page 42
CAMOUFLAGE CAM
There are 10 Green Rangers.

Page 43
TALL ORDER

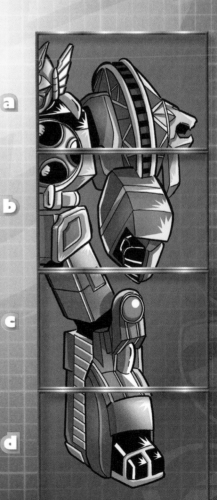

a

b

c

d